A DIFFERENT STORY

Poems From The Past

Selected by Michael Rosen

Acknowledgements

Selection by Michael Rosen with Barbara Bleiman, Sabrina Broadbent and Emma Henderson.
Activities by Barbara Bleiman.
Additional Material by John Stephens and Sabrina Broadbent.
Anthology Edited by Barbara Bleiman.

Design: Fran Stowell.
Front Cover: Dave Bradshaw.

Printed by BPC Wheatons.
ISBN 0 907016 05 7

Introduction

In schools and colleges, collections of poetry are often put before us to study. When these are collections of several poets, then the book makes a statement like 'these poems are worth studying' or 'this is what poetry is'. So what kind of poetry do we find in such books? Nearly always it has been poems by people who are regarded by teachers in universities as 'great'. Anyone who has studied English at university can recite their names like a nursery rhyme: Chaucer, Shakespeare, Donne, Pope, Coleridge, Wordsworth, Keats, Shelley, Byron, Browning, Tennyson, Eliot, Auden, Hughes, Heaney. But if this is the only poetry we read, a lot gets left out. Hidden from view over hundreds of years have been other kinds of poetry. That is the underlying idea of this anthology: to present some poems that have been hidden away. So why have they been hidden? Where? What kinds of people wrote them?

Some were hidden because they were women, some because they were poor, some because they weren't written down in books, some because they were thought to be dangerous. Some of these people, like Daniel Defoe, the author of *Robinson Crusoe* are names known all over the world for their writing, even if the poem in this collection is not one often seen. Others are people 'discovered' in recent years, their writing having lain about in libraries for years. Aphra Behn, playwright, novelist, poet and spy was missing from English syllabuses for years. There are plenty of examples of 'anon' here too, which can mean, 'nobody knows who sat down and wrote this,' or 'it wasn't written by any *one* person but was changed and shaped by many people as it was passed on'. This means that very unfamous people have been involved in making some of the poems here: peasants, slaves, miners, tombstone makers, say, and a rather strange breed of person, the ballad-seller, someone who made his living travelling about the country with a pack of poems on funny, tragic themes or topical events to sell them to make a living.

So, what we have here is not easily given a label or a pigeon-hole in the way literary books usually are. But one way to look at it is to say that things that are hidden away are often surprising, strange, exciting and different.

Michael Rosen

Contents

	Page	Activity
An Anglo-Saxon Riddle	6	94
Death	7	
A Betrayed Maiden's Lament	8	
On Nought	9	
The Covetous Man	10	97
Wicked Tongues	12	
A Servant Girl's Holiday	14	
The Schoolboy	16	99
The Death of Queen Jane	18	110
Out of Sight, Out of Mind	20	
Brissit Brawnis	21	
The Passionate Shepherd to His Love	22	100
The Nymph's Reply to the Shepherd	23	100
The Furies	24	125
The Lowest Trees Have Tops	25	
Of Treason	26	
These Fatlings Feast	26	
This Island's Mine	27	
The Hill to Hell	28	
On My Boy Henry	30	
The Wooing Rogue	31	100
On Tobacco	32	
What Faith?	34	
A House She Hath	35	
A North Midlands 'Miners' Law' Verse	35	
Song: The Willing Mistress	36	
'The Art of Love' - Instructions to a Man	37	
Rich and Poor	38	
Trail All Your Pikes	38	125
A Last Will and Testament	39	
What is an Englishman?	42	
To the Ladies	44	103
Clever Tom Clinch Going To Be Hanged	45	112
The Dream	46	
A Beautiful Young Nymph Going to Bed	47	105
Epigram on the Collar of a Dog	50	
In Memory of Mr. Peter Daniels	50	
Here Lies Fred	51	
A Woman to Her Lover	52	
Midas's Touch	53	
A Glazier's Verse	53	

	Page	Activity
Here Lie I	54	
Guinea Corn	55	
The Fate of Those Who Go for Soldiers	56	125
The Volunteer	58	125
Supper is Na Ready	60	
The Common and the Goose	60	
The Pottery Worker	61	
The Twa Corbies	62	
What is Slavery?	64	
The Factory Girl's Last Day	66	
Epitaph to Castlereagh	68	
Ah Sidney!	68	
The Foddering Boy	69	108
The Engineer's Epitaph	70	109
The Fine, Old English Gentleman	71	
No!	73	
The Recruited Collier	74	125
Monster Science	76	
The Slave Mother	78	
We Raise The Wheat	80	
What I Know Is Me	80	
My Lord Tomnoddy	81	
The Factory Bell	84	
Two Strings to a Bow	86	
Is it Fair?	86	
The Greatest Bore	87	
Some English Prisons	87	
A London Fete	88	112
Cork and Work and Card and Ward	90	
Fight? What For?	91	125
John Bun	91	
The Death of Queen Jane	92	110
Activities Section	93	
Activities on Individual Poems	94	
Work on the Anthology as a Whole	113	
Exploring a Poem	114	
Performing Poems	117	
Re-organising the Anthology into Themes	121	
Making Your Own Selection of Poems	122	
Disgusted of Tunbridge Wells	124	
Poems About War and Soldiering	125	

An Anglo-Saxon Riddle

Moððe word frǣt;   mē þæt þūhte
wrǣtlicu wyrd,   þā ic þæt wundor gefrægn,
þæt se wyrm forswealg   wera gied sumes,
þēof in þȳstro   þrymfæstne cwide
and þæs strangan staþol.   Stælgiest ne wæs
wihte þȳ glēawra   þē hē þām wordum swealg.

Moth word ate   me that thought

amazing event   when I that wonder heard

that the worm swallowed   man word of a

thief in darkness   glorious saying

and that strong foundation   steal-guest (i.e. thief) not was

whit the wiser   when he those words swallowed

Anon, c. 975

Death

Whenne mine eynen misteth
And mine eren sisseth[1]
And my nose coldeth
And my tunge foldeth[2]
And my rude slaketh[3]
And mine lippes blaketh[4]
And my mouth grenneth[5]
And my spotel renneth[6]
And myn her riseth[7]
And myn herte griseth[8]
And mine handen bivieth[9]
And mine feet stivieth[10]
Al to late, al to late
Whenne the bere[11] is at the gate!
Thenne I shal flit
From bedde to flore,
From flore to here,[12]
From here to bere,
From bere to pit,
And the pit fordit,[13]
Thenne lith myn hous uppe[14] myn nese:
Of al this world ne give ich a pese![15]

Anon, c.1275-1300

1. hiss
2. fails, folds up
3. my colour fades
4. grow pale
5. gapes? grins?
6. my spittle runs
7. stands on end
8. quakes
9. shake
10. stiffen
11. bier
12. hair-shroud
13. will shut
14. upon
15. a pea

A Betrayed Maiden's Lament

I haue for-sworne hit whil I life
to wake the well-ey.[1]

The last tyme I the wel woke[2]
Ser Iohn caght me with a croke,
he made me to swere be bel & boke[3]
  I shuld not tell [-ey.]

Yet he did me a wel wors turne,
he leyde my hed agayn the burne,[4]
he gafe my mayden-hed a spurne[5]
  and rofe my kell [-ey.][6]

Sir Iohn came to oure hows to play
ffro evensong tyme til light of the day;
we made as mery as flowres in may—
  I was begyled-ay.

Sir Iohn he came to our hows,
he made hit wondur copious[7]
he seyd that I was gracious[8]
  to beyre a childe-ey.

I go with childe, wel I wot;[9]
I schrew[10] the fadur that hit gate,
with-outen[11] he fynde hit mylke and pap
  a long while-ey.

Anon, c.1350

1. I have given up doing it when I spend the night, for as long as I live.
2. spent the night
3. by the bell and the book (the Bible)
4. well
5. a stroke
6. took my virginity
7. brought lots of presents
8. lucky
9. I know full well
10. curse
11. unless

On Nought

He that spendes myche & getes nothing,
And owthe myche & hathe nothing,
And lokes in his porse & fyndes nothing,
he may be sorye and saie nothing.
Quothe K.L.

Anon, c.1350

The Covetous Man

This is an extract from Langland's long poem Piers Plowman. It is an imaginary story of a ploughman who has a dream in which he travels around the medieval world, seeing all kinds of dreadful behaviour, particularly from members of the church. Langland felt that the church had become too concerned with making money and had lost its spiritual values. On his travels, Piers meets each of the Seven Deadly Sins, who are presented as people.

And thanne cam Coveitise. Can I him nought descrive,
So hungriliche and holwe sire Hervy him looked.[1]
He was bitelbrowed and baberlipped also,[2]
With two blered eyghen as a blinde hagge;
And as a letheren purs lolled his chekes,
Wel sidder than his chin[3] they chiveled for elde;[4]
And as a bondman[5] of his bacoun his berde was bidraveled;[6]
With an hoode on his hed, a lousy[7] hatte above,
And in a tawny tabarde of twelve winter age,
Al totorne and baudy[8] and ful of lis creepinge;
But if that a lous couthe have lopen[9] the bettre,
She sholde noughte have walked on that welche,[10] so was it thredebare.

William Langland, c.1360

1. he looked like Sir Harvey (nickname for a greedy cheat),
2. beetle-browed and blubbery-lipped
3. lower than his chin
4. trembled with age
5. like a servant or labourer
6. matted with bacon grease
7. full of lice
8. ragged and dirty
9. unless a louse could jump better
10. welsh flannel

5
Inuidia atra lues, successibus aspera faustis,
Ipsa fit infælix carnificina sui.

Wicked Tongues

Keep thy tunge, thy tunge, thy tunge;
Thy wiked tunge werketh me wo.[1]

Ther is none gres[2] that groweth on ground,
Satenas[3] ne peny-round,
Werse than is a wikked tunge
That speketh bothe evil of frend and fo.

Wikked tunge maketh ofte strif
Betwix a good-man[4] and his wif;
When he shulde lede a merye lif
Her white sides waxen ful blo.[5]

Wikked tunge maketh ofte staunce,[6]
Bothe in Engelond and in Fraunce;
Many a man with spere and launce
Through wikked tunge to ded is do.[7]

Wikked tunge breketh bone,
Though the self[8] have none;
Of his frend he maketh his fone[9]
In every place wher that he go.

Good men that sitten in this halle,
I pray you, bothe one and alle,
That wikked tunges fro you falle,
That ye mowen to hevne go.

Anon, c.1450

1. gives me grief
2. herb
3. a poisonous plant
4. husband
5. her white sides become black and blue, (he beats her)
6. causes disputes
7. done to death
8. though it itself
9. enemies

A Servant Girl's Holiday

Ribbe ne rele ne spinne ich ne may[1]
For joye that it is holiday.

Al this day ich han sought;[2]
Spindel ne werve[3] no fond I nought;
To miche blisse ich am brought
Ayen[4] this highe holiday.

Al unswope is oure flet,[5]
And oure fire is unbet;[6]
Oure rushen ben unrepe yet
Ayen this highe holiday.

Ich moste fechen worten[7] in;
Predele[8] my kerchef under my chin -
Leve[9] Jacke, lend me a pin
To predele me this holiday.

Now it draweth to the none,
And al my cherres[10] ben undone;
I moste a lite solas my shone[11]
To make hem douse[12] this holiday.

I moste milken in this pail;
Ought me bred al this shail;[13]
Yet is the dow[14] under my nail
As ich knad[15] this holiday.

Jacke wol bringe me onward in my wey,
With me desire for to pleye;
Of my dame stant me non ay
On never a good holiday.[16]

Jacke wol pay for my scot[17]
A Sonday at the ale-scot;[18]
Jacke wol souse wel my throt
Every good holiday.

Soone he wold take me by the hond,
And he wol legge[19] me on the lond
That al my buttockes ben of sond
Upon this highe holiday.

In he pult and out he drow,
And ever ich lay on him y-low:[20]
'By Godes deth, thow dest me wow[21]
Upon this highe holiday!'

Soone my wombe began to swelle
As gret as a belle;
Durst I nat my dame telle
What me betidde this holiday.

Anon, 1475

1. I cannot scrape flax or reel thread or spin
2. I've been looking for things
3. whorl for spinning
4. waiting for
5. our floor is unswept
6. not made up
7. vegetables
8. fasten
9. dear
10. chores
11. soften my shoes a little
12. comfortable
13. I ought to lay out the crockery? leave the dough to rise?
14. dough
15. kneaded
16. I'm not afraid of my mistress on any good holiday
17. share of the bill
18. the Sunday pay-for-yourself feast
19. lay
20. I'm lying beneath him
21. do me wrong

The Schoolboy

Hay, hay, by this day,
What availeth it me[1] though I say nay?

I wold fain be a clerke,[2]
But yet it is a stronge[3] werke;
The birchen twigges be so sharpe
It makith me have a faint herte.
What availeth it me though I say nay?

On Monday in the morning when I shall rise,
At six of the clok, it is the gise[4]
To go to scole without avise -[5]
I had lever[6] go twenty mile twise.
What availeth it me though I say nay?

My master lookith as he were madde:
'Wher hast thou be, thou sory ladde?'
'Milke dukkes my moder badde' -[7]
It was no mervaile though I were sadde.
What availeth it me though I say nay?

My master pepered my ars with well good spede;
It was worse than finkill sede;[8]
He wold not leve till it did blede -
Miche sorow have he for his dede!
What availeth it me though I say nay?

I wold my master were a watt,[9]
And my booke a wild catt,
And a brase of grehoundes in his toppe:[10]
I wold be glad for to see that!
What availeth it me though I say nay?

I wold my master were an hare,
And all his bookes houndes were,

And I myself a joly huntere;
To blow my horn I wold not spare,
For if he were dede I wold not care.
What availeth it me though I say nay?

Anon, c.1520

1. what use is it to me
2. I would like to be a scholar
3. painful
4. custom
5. without a question
6. rather
7. my mother told me to milk the ducks
8. fennel seed
9. a wild hare
10. after him

The Death of Queen Jane

Queen Jane was in travail[1]
For six weeks or more,
Till the women grew tired,
And fain would give o'er.[2]
'O women! O women!
Good wives if ye be,
Go, send for King Henrie,
And bring him to me.'

King Henrie was sent for,
He came with all speed,
In a gownd of green velvet
From heel to the head.
'King Henrie! King Henrie!
If kind Henrie you be,
Send for a surgeon,
And bring him to me.'

The surgeon was sent for,
He came with all speed,
In a gownd of black velvet
From heel to the head.
He gave her rich caudle,[3]
But the death-sleep slept she.
Then her right side was opened,
And the babe was set free.

The babe it was christened,
And put out and nursed,
While the royal Queen Jane
She lay cold in the dust.

So black was the mourning,
And white were the wands,
Yellow, yellow the torches,

They bore in their hands.
The bells they were muffled,
And mournful did play,
While the royal Queen Jane
She lay cold in the clay.

Six knights and six lords
Bore her corpse through the grounds;
Six dukes followed after,
In black mourning gownds.
The flower of Old England
Was laid in cold clay,
Whilst the royal King Henrie
Came weeping away.

Anon, c.1540

1. labour
2. would have liked to give up
3. a warm alcoholic drink

Out of Sight, Out of Mind

The oftener seen, the more I lust,
  The more I lust, the more I smart,
The more I smart, the more I trust,
  The more I trust, the heavier heart,
The heavy heart breeds mine unrest,
Thy absence therefore like I best.

The rarer seen, the less in mind,
  The less in mind, the lesser pain,
The lesser pain, less grief I find,
  The lesser grief, the greater gain,
The greater gain, the merrier I,
Therefore I wish thy sight to fly.

The further off, the more I joy,
  The more I joy, the happier life,
The happier life, less hurts annoy,
  The lesser hurts, pleasure most rife,
Such pleasures rife shall I obtain
When distance doth depart us twain.[1]

Barnabe Googe , 1563

1. two

Brissit Brawnis

Brissit brawnis[1] and broken banis[2]
Strif, discord, and wastie wanis,[3]
Crukit in eld, sin halt withall:[4]
Thir[5] are the bewteis of the fut-ball.

Anon, c.1575

1. bruised muscles
2. bones
3. desolate homes
4. crooked in old age and lame too
5. these

The Passionate Shepherd to His Love

Come live with me and be my Love,
And we will all the pleasures prove
That hills and valleys, dales and fields,
Or woods or steepy mountain yields.

And we will sit upon the rocks,
And see the shepherds feed their flocks
By shallow rivers, to whose falls
Melodious birds sing madrigals.

And I will make thee beds of roses,
And a thousand fragrant posies;
A cap of flowers, and a kirtle[1]
Embroider'd all with leaves of myrtle.

A gown made of the finest wool
Which from our pretty lambs we pull;
Fair-lined slippers for the cold,
With buckles of the purest gold,

A belt of straw and ivy-buds,
With coral clasps, and amber studs;
And if these pleasures may thee move,
Come live with me and be my Love.

The shepherd swains shall dance and sing
For they delight, each May morning:
If these delights thy mind may move,
Then live with me, and be my Love.

Christopher Marlowe, 1600

1. skirt

The Nymph's Reply to the Shepherd

If all the world and love were young,
And truth in every shepherd's tongue,
Those pretty pleasures might me move
To live with thee and by thy Love.

Time drives the flocks from field to fold,
When rivers rage and rocks grow cold;
And Philomel[1] becometh dumb;
The rest complains of cares to come.

The flowers do fade, and wanton fields
To wayward winter reckoning yields:
A honey tongue, a heart of gall,
Is fancy's spring, but sorrow's fall.

Thy gowns, thy shoes, thy beds of roses,
Thy cap, thy kirtle, and thy posies
Soon break, soon wither, soon forgotten,
In folly ripe, in reason rotten.

Thy belt of straw and ivy buds,
Thy coral clasps and amber studs,
All these in me no means can move
To come to thee and be thy Love.

But could youth last, and love still breed,
Had joys no date, nor age no need,
Then these delights my mind might move
To live with thee and be thy Love.

Sir Walter Raleigh, c. 1600

1. In Greek legend, Philomel was raped by her brother-in-law, who cut out her tongue

The Furies

War is the mistress of enormity,
Mother of mischief, monster of deformity;
Laws, manners, arts she breaks, she mars, she chases,
Blood, tears, bowers,[1] towers, she spills, smites, burns, and razes.
Her brazen teeth shake all the earth asunder:
Her mouth a firebrand, and her voice a thunder,
Her looks are lightning, every glance a flash,
Her fingers guns that all to powder smash;
Fear and despair, flight and disorder, post[2]
With hasty march before her murderous host.
As burning, waste, rape, wrong, impiety,
Rage, ruin, discord, horror, cruelty,
Sack,[3] sacrilege, impunity and pride are still stern consorts by her barbarous side;
And poverty, sorrow, and desolation
Follow her armies' bloody transmigration.

Joshua Sylvester, c.1598

1. dwellings
2. hurry
3. looting

The Lowest Trees Have Tops

The lowest trees have tops; the ant her gall;
  The fly her spleen;[1] the little sparks their heat;
The slender hairs cast shadows, though but small;
  And bees have stings, although they be not great.
Seas have their source, and so have shallow springs;
And love is love, in beggars as in kings.

Where rivers smoothest run, deep are the fords;
  The dial[2] stirs, yet none perceives it move;
The firmest faith is in the fewest words;
  The turtles cannot sing, and yet they love.
True hearts have eyes and ears, no tongues to speak;
They hear and see, and sigh; and then they break.

Edward Dyer, 1599

1. part of the stomach, thought to be responsible for temper or bad moods
2. sundial

Of Treason

Treason doth never prosper: What's the reason?
For if it prosper, none dare call it treason.

Sir John Harington, c.1600

These Fatlings Feast

These fatlings feast, while as I poorly fast,
They dine, I pine; they sweetly sleep, I wake:
They leave, I lack; I want, they plenty waste:
I seek a crumb, while choice of cates[1] they make,
  Their fast is dearth of stomach, not of meat,[2]
  Mine is because I have not what to eat.

Arthur Warren, 1605

1. delicacies, sweetmeats
2. lack of interest in eating, rather than lack of food

This Island's Mine

This is an extract from Shakespeare's play, 'The Tempest'. Caliban is an inhabitant of an island. Duke Prospero lands there after he has been banished from Milan, in Italy and takes control of the island, making Caliban his slave. In this speech Caliban is talking to Prospero.

CALIBAN: This island's mine, by Sycorax my mother,
Which thou tak'st from me. When thou cam'st first,
Thou strok'st me, and made much of me; wouldst
give me
Water with berries in't; and teach me how
To name the bigger light, and how the less,
That burn by day and night:[1] and then I lov'd thee,
And show'd thee all the qualities o'th'isle,
The fresh springs, brine-pits,[2] barren place and fertile:
Curs'd be I that did so! All the charms
Of Sycorax, toads, beetles, bats, light on you!
For I am all the subjects that you have,
Which first was mine own King: and here you sty me
In this hard rock, whiles you do keep from me
The rest o' th' island.

From ***The Tempest***, *William Shakespeare, 1611*

1. the sun and the moon
2. sources of salty water

The Hill to Hell

Now to thy rest, 'tis night. But here approaches
A troop with torches, hurried in their coaches.
Stay and behold, what are they? I can tell,
Some bound for Shoreditch, or for Clerkenwell;
Oh these are they which think that fornication
Is but a youthful, sportful, recreation;
These, to hold out the game, maintain the back
With marrow pies, potato roots, and sack;
And when that nature hath consumed her part,
Can hold out a luxurious course by art.[1]
Go, stop the horses quickly (lest thou miss)
And tell the coachman's wanton[2] carriage this,
They of their guide must be advised well,
For they are running down the hill to hell.
Their venery will soon consume their stocks,[3]
And bring them to repentance with a pox.[4]

George Wither, 1613

1. To keep going sexually, these people use all kinds of aphrodisiacs and arts, to add to what nature gave them
2. lustful
3. their lustfulness will soon use up their life-store
4. sexually transmitted disease

On my Boy Henry

Here lyes a Boy ye finest child from me
Which makes my Heart & Soul sigh for to see
Nor can I think of any thought, but greeve,
For joy or pleasure could me not releeve,
It lived dayes as many as my years,
No more; wich caused my greeved teares;
Twenty and Nine was the number;
And death hath parted us asunder,
But you art happy, Sweet'st on High,
I mourne not for thy Birth, nor Cry.

Elizabeth Egerton, Countess of Bridgewater, 1656

The Wooing Rogue

Come live with me and be my Whore,
And we will beg from door to door
Then under a hedge we'l sit and louse[1] us,
Until the Beadle[2] come to rouse us
And if they'l give us no relief;
  Thou shalt turn Whore and I'l turn Thief.
  Thou shalt turn Whore and I'l turn Thief.

If thou canst rob, then I can steal,
And we'l eat Roast-meat every meal:
Nay, we'l eat white-bread every day
And throw our mouldy crusts away,
And twice a day we will be drunk,
  And then at night I'l kiss my Punk,[3]
  And then at night I'l kiss my Punk.

And when we both shall have the Pox,
We then shall want[4] both Shirts and Smocks,
To shift[5] each others mangy hide,
That is with Itch so pockifi'd;
We'l take some clean ones from a hedge,
  And leave our old ones for a pledge.[6]
  And leave our old ones for a pledge.

Anon, c.1660

1. de-louse us
2. a policeman
3. whore
4. lack
5. clothe
6. a loan guarantee

On Tobacco

What nameless ill does its contagion shroud
In the dark mantle of this noisome cloud?
Sure 'tis the Devil; Oh, I know that's it,
Foh! How the sulphur makes me cough and spit!
'Tis he; or else some fav'rite fiend at least,
In all the mischief of his malice dressed;
Each deadly sin that lurks t'entrap the soul,
Does here concealed in curling vapours roll,
And for the body such an unknown ill,
As makes physicians' reading,[1] and their skill:
One undistinguished pest made up of all
That men experienced do diseases call:
Coughs, asthmas, apoplexies, fevers, rheum,[2]
All that kill dead, or lingeringly consume,
Folly, and madness, nay the plague, the pox;
And ev'ry fool wears a Pandora's box.[3]
From that rich mine, the stupid sot doth fill,
Smokes up his liver, and his lungs, until
His reeking nostrils monstrously proclaim,
His brains, and bowels are consuming flame.
What noble soul would be content to dwell
In the dark lanthorn[4] of a smoky cell?
To prostitute his body, and his mind,
To a debauch of such a stinking kind?
To sacrifice to Moloch,[5] and to fry,
In such a base, dirty idolatry;
As if frail life, which of itself's too short,
Were to be whiffed away in drunken sport?
Thus, as if weary of our destined years,
We burn the thread so to prevent the shears.[6]

Charles Cotton, c.1660

1. tests out the doctors' knowledge
2. a cold
3. In the Greek legend, Pandora disobeyed the gods, opened the box and let out all the evil things that plague human beings.
4. lantern
5. an idol or false god
6. prevent death from killing us in its own time by killing ourselves first

What Faith?

A broadside posted in a country inn in Gloucestershire. (Read down the two columns, the verses are Roman Catholic in sentiment, read straight across they are Anglican).

I hold as faith
What *Rome's* church saith
Where the *King's* head[2]
The flocks misled
Where the *altars* drest
The peoples blest
He's but an asse
Who shuns the *masse*

What *England's church* alows
My conscience disavows[1]
That *church* can have no shame
That holds the *Pope* supreame.
There's service scarce divine
With table, bread and wine.
Who the *communion* flies
Is *catholick* and wise.

Anon, c.1665

1. says is wrong
2. the king is the official head of the Church of England, which broke away from the Roman Catholic Church over a hundred years before this poem was written

A House She Hath

A house she hath, it's made of such good fashion
The tenant ne'er shall pay for reparation:[1]
Nor will the Landlord ever raise the rent,
Or turn her out of doors for non-payment
From chimney money[2] too, this cell is free
To such a house as this who would not tenant be.

Rebecca Rogers' epitaph, Folkestone, 1688

1. repairs
2. a kind of tax

A North Midlands 'Miners' Law' Verse

For stealing oar[1] twice from the minery,
The thief that's taken twice fined shall be,
But the third time that he commits such theft,
Shall have a knife stuck through his hand to th' haft,[2]
Into the stow,[3] and there to death shall stand,
Or loose himself by cutting loose his hand,
And shall forswear the franchise of the mine,[4]
And always lose his freedom from that time.

Anon, Seventeenth Century

1. ore
2. handle
3. stove
4. give up the right to mine there

Song: The Willing Mistress

Amyntas[1] led me to a Grove,
Where all the Trees did shade us;
The Sun it self, though it had Strove,
It could not have betray'd us:

The place secur'd from humane Eyes,
No other fear allows,
But when the Winds that gently rise,
Doe Kiss the yeilding Boughs.

Down there we satt upon the Moss,
And did begin to play
A Thousand Amorous Tricks, to pass
The heat of all the day.
A many Kisses he did give:
And I return'd the same
Which made me willing to receive
That which I dare not name.

His Charming Eyes no aid requir'd
To tell their softning Tale;
On her that was already fir'd
'Twas Easy to prevaile.
He did but Kiss and Clasp me round
Whilst those his thoughts Exprest:
And lay'd me gently on the Ground;
Ah who can guess the rest?

Aphra Behn, c.1670

1. an ancient Greek king. When this poem was written it was fashionable to use ancient classical names in love poems

'The Art of Love' - Instructions to a Man

Be not too finical;[1] but yet be clean;
And wear well-fashioned clothes, like other men.
Let not your teeth be yellow, or be foul;
Nor in wide shoes your feet too loosely roul.[2]
Of a black muzzle,[3] and long beard beware;
And let a skilful barber cut your hair:
Your nails be picked from filth, and even pared;
Nor let your nasty nostrils bud with beard.
Cure your unsavoury breath; gargle your throat;
And free your armpits from the ram and goat.
Dress not, in short, too little, or too much:
And be not wholly French, nor wholly Dutch.

From the Latin poet Ovid (43 BC - 17 AD). Translated by John Dryden in the Seventeenth Century

1. finicky
2. roll
3. nose and mouth

Rich and Poor

This world is a city full of streets
And Death the merchant that all men meets.
If life were a thing that money could buy,
The poor could not live and the rich would not die.

From Elgin Cathedral, 1689

Trail All Your Pikes

Trail all your pikes, dispirit every drum,
March in a slow procession from afar,
Ye silent, ye dejected men of war!
Be still the hautboys,[1] and the flute be dumb!
Display no more, in vain, the lofty banner.
For see! where on the bier before ye lies
The pale, the fall'n, th'untimely sacrifice
To your mistaken shrine, to your false idol Honour!

Anne Finch, Countess of Winchelsea, 1662-1720

1. musical instrument, like an oboe

A Last Will and Testament

To my dear wife,
My joy and life,
I freely now do give her
  My whole estate,
  With all my plate,
Being just about to leave her.

A tub of soap,
A long cart-rope,
A frying-pan and kettle;
  An ashes pail,
  A threshing flail,
An iron wedge and beetle.

Two painted chairs,
Nine warden pears,
A large old dripping platter;
  The bed of hay,
  On which I lay,
An old saucepan for butter.

A little mug,
A two-quart jug,
A bottle full of brandy;
  A looking-glass,
  To see your face,
You'll find it very handy.

A musket true
As ever flew,
A pound of shot, and wallet;
  A leather sash,
  My calabash,
My powder-horn, and bullet.

An old sword-blade,
A garden spade,
A hoe, a rake, a ladder,
  A wooden can,
  A close-stool pan,
A clyster-pipe,[1] and bladder.

A greasy hat,
My old ram-cat,
A yard and half of linen;
  A pot of grease,
  A woollen fleece,
In order for your spinning.

A small toothcomb,
An ashen broom,
A candlestick, and hatchet;
  A coverlid,[2]
Striped down with red,
A bag of rags to patch it.
A ragged mat,
A tub of fat,
A book, put out by Bunyan,[3]
  Another book,
  By Robin Rook,[4]
A skein, or two, of spun yarn.

An old black muff,
Some garden stuff,
A quantity of borage;
  Some Devil's-weed,
  And burdock seed,
To season well your porridge.

A chafing-dish,[5]
With one salt fish,
If I am not mistaken;
  A leg of pork,
  A broken fork,
And half a flitch of bacon.

A spinning-wheel,
One peck of meal;
A knife without a handle;
  A rusty lamp,
  Two quarts of samp,[6]
And half a tallow candle.

My pouch and pipes,
Two oxen tripes,
An oaken dish well carved;
  My little dog,
  And spotted hog,
With two young pigs just starved.

This is my store,
I have no more,
I heartily do give it;
  My days are spun,
  My life is done,
And so I think to leave it.

John Winstanley, c.1700

1. a pipe inserted in the anus to relieve constipation
2. bedcover
3. John Bunyan's 'The Pilgrim's Progress', a much read book at the time
4. a name for a cheat?
5. a container to keep food warm
6. porridge made of sweetcorn

What is an Englishman?

This is an extract from a poem, written in support of William of Orange, who was the King of England at the time but was German by birth.

Thus from a mixture of all kinds began
That het'rogeneous thing, an Englishman,
In eager rapes, and furious lust begot
Betwixt a painted Briton and a Scot;
Whose gend'ring offspring quickly learnt to bow,
And yoke their heifers to the Roman plough,
From whence a mongrel half-bred race there came,
With neither name nor nation, speech or fame,
In whose hot veins new mixtures quickly ran,
Infused betwixt a Saxon and a Dane,
While their rank daughters, to their parents just,
Received all nations with promiscuous lust.
This nauseous brood directly did contain
The well-extracted blood of Englishmen.

Which medly cantoned in a heptarchy,[1]
A rhapsody of nations to supply,
Among themselves maintained eternal wars,
And still the ladies loved the conquerors.

The Western Angles all the rest subdued,
A bloody nation, barbarous and rude,
Who by the tenure of the sword possessed
One part of Britain, and subdued the rest.
And as great things denominate the small,
The conqu'ring part gave title to the whole.
The Scot, Pict, Briton, Roman, Dane submit,
And with the English-Saxon all unite:
And these the mixture have so close pursued,
The very name and memory's subdued:
No Roman now, no Briton does remain;
Wales strove to separate, but strove in vain:
The silent nations undistinguished fall,
And Englishman's the common name for all.

Fate jumbled them together, God knows how;
Whate'er they were, they're True-born English now.

Daniel Defoe, 1701

1. the heptarchy was the seven kingdoms into which Anglo-Saxon England was divided

To the Ladies

Wife and servant are the same
But only differ in the name:
For when that fatal knot is tied,
Which nothing, nothing can divide,
When she the word *Obey* has said,
And man by law supreme has made,
Then all that's kind is laid aside,
And nothing left but state and pride.
Fierce as an eastern prince he grows,
And all his innate rigour shows:
Then but to look, to laugh, or speak,
Will the nuptial contract break.
Like mutes, she sighs alone must make,
And never any freedom take,
But still be governed by a nod,
And fear her husband as her god:
Him still must serve, him still obey,
And nothing act, and nothing say,
But what her haughty lord thinks fit,
Who, with the power, has all the wit.
Then shun, oh! shun that wretched state,
And all the fawning flatt'rers hate.
Value yourselves, and men despise:
You must be proud, if you'll be wise.

Mary, Lady Chudleigh, 1703

Clever Tom Clinch Going To Be Hanged

As clever Tom Clinch, while the rabble was bawling,
Rode stately through Holborn,[1] to die in his calling;[2]
He stopped at the George for a bottle of sack,
And promised to pay for it when he'd come back.
His waistcoat and stockings and breeches were white,
His cap had a new cherry ribbon to tie't.
The maids to the doors and the balconies ran,
And said, 'Lack-a-day! He's a proper young man!'
But, as from the windows the ladies he spied,
Like a beau in a box,[3] he bowed low to each side;
And when his last speech the loud hawkers[4] did cry,
He swore from his cart, it was all a damned lie.
The hangman for pardon fell down on his knee;
Tom gave him a kick in the guts for his fee.
Then said, 'I must speak to the people a little,
But I'll see you all damned before I will whittle.[5]
My honest friend Wild,[6] may he long hold his place,
He lengthened my life with a whole year of grace.
Take courage, dear comrades, and be not afraid,
Nor slip this occasion to follow your trade.
My conscience is clear, and my spirits are calm,
And thus I go off without prayer-book or psalm.
Then follow the practice of clever Tom Clinch,
Who hung like a hero, and never would flinch.'

Jonathan Swift , 1726

1. a district of London. The procession went from Newgate prison, through Holborn, to Tyburn where the execution would take place
2. his profession as a thief
3. a handsome man in a box at the theatre
4. street sellers, who sold 'dying speeches', supposedly the last words of the person about to be hanged
5. thieves' slang for confessing at the gallows
6. a famous thief-taker, who was finally executed himself

The Dream

I dreamed that, buried in my fellow clay,
Close by a common beggar's side I lay;
And as so mean a neighbour shocked my pride,
Thus, like a corpse of consequence, I cried:
'Scoundrel, begone, and henceforth touch me not;
More manners learn, and at a distance rot.'
'How, scoundrel!' in a haughtier tone cried he:
'Proud lump of dirt, I scorn thy words and thee.
Here all are equal, now thy case is mine:
This is my rotting-place, and that is thine.'

Anon, 1727

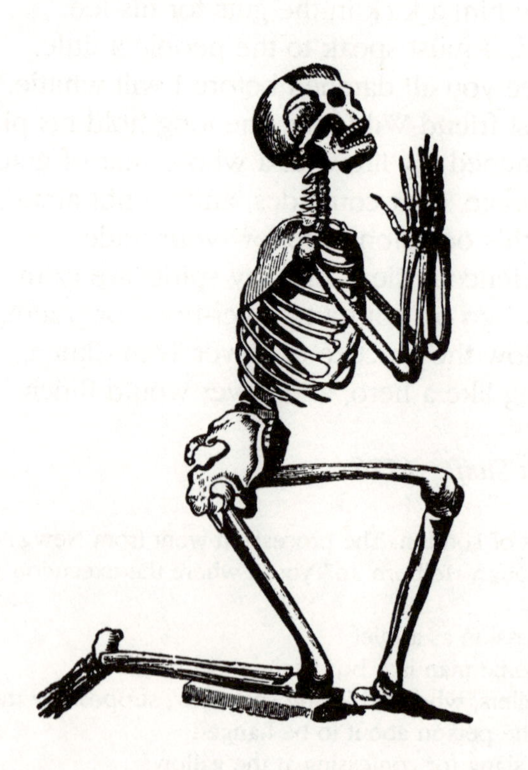

A Beautiful Young Nymph Going To Bed

WRITTEN FOR THE HONOUR OF THE FAIR SEX

Corinna, pride of Drury Lane,[1]
For whom no shepherd sighs in vain;
Never did Covent Garden[2] boast
So bright a battered, strolling toast;
No drunken rake to pick her up,
No cellar where on tick to sup;
Returning at the midnight hour;
Four stories climbing to her bower;
Then, seated on a three-legged chair,
Takes off her artificial hair:
Now, picking out a crystal eye,
She wipes it clean, and lays it by.
Her eye-brows from a mouse's hide,
Stuck on with art on either side,
Pulls off with care, and first displays 'em,
Then in a play-book smoothly lays 'em.
Now dextrously her plumpers[3] draws,
That serve to fill her hollow jaws.
Untwists a wire; and from her gums
A set of teeth completely comes.
Pulls out the rags contrived to prop
Her flabby dugs[4] and down they drop.
Proceeding on, the lovely goddess
Unlaces next her steel-ribbed bodice;
Which by the operator's skill,
Press down the lumps, the hollows fill,
Up goes her hand, and off she slips
The bolsters that supply her hips.
With gentlest touch, she next explores
Her shankers,[5] issues, running sores,
Effects of many a sad disaster;
And then to each applies a plaster.
But must, before she goes to bed,

Rub off the daubs with white and red;
And smooth the furrows in her front,[6]
With greasy paper stuck upon't.
She takes a bolus[7] ere she sleeps;
And then between two blankets creeps.
With pains of love tormented lies;
Or if she chance to close her eyes,
Of Bridewell[8] and the Compter[9] dreams,
And feels the lash, and faintly screams;
Or, by a faithless bully[10] drawn,
At some hedge-tavern[11] lies in pawn;
Or to Jamaica[12] seems transported
Alone, and by no planter courted;
Or, near Fleet Ditch's[13] oozy brinks,
Surrounded with a hundred stinks,
Belated, seems on watch to lie,
And snap some cully[14] passing by;
Or, struck with fear, her fancy runs
On watchmen, constables and duns,[15]
For whom she meets with frequent rubs;[16]
But, never from religious clubs;[17]
Whose favour she is sure to find,
Because she pays them all in kind.
  Corinna wakes. A dreadful sight!
Behold the ruins of the night!
A wicked rat her plaster stole,
Half ate, and dragged it to his hold.
The crystal eye, alas, was missed;
And puss had on her plumpers pissed.
A pigeon picked her issue-peas;[18]
And Shock her tresses filled with fleas.
  The nymph, though in this mangled plight,
Must every morn her limbs unite.
But how shall I describe her arts
To recollect the scattered parts?
Or show the anguish, toil, and pain,
Of gathering up herself again?
The bashful Muse[19] will never bear

In such a scene to interfere.
Corinna in the morning dizened,[20]
Who sees, will spew; who smells, be poisoned.

Jonathan Swift, 1734

1. a street in London, at this time well-known as an area for prostitutes
2. near Drury Lane, with the same reputation
3. a small ball carried in the mouth to fill out hollow cheeks. Venereal disease caused the teeth to rot
4. breasts
5. sores caused by venereal disease
6. forehead
7. a large pill
8. a prison for women vagrants and prostitutes
9. a city prison, possibly for people in debt
10. a pimp
11. a poor pub
12. some 'criminals' were transported to Jamaica
13. a dirty river running into the Thames
14. grab some fool
15. people who are always trying to get back the money they are owed
16. unpleasant meetings
17. religious clubs for people who don't conform to the official Catholic or Anglican Church
18. a medical instrument to drain off pus from a cut
19. the goddess who inspires writers to write poetry
20. dressed

Epigram on the Collar of a Dog

I am his Highness'[1] dog at Kew;[2]
Pray tell me, sir, whose dog are you?

Alexander Pope, 1738

1. King George II
2. a part of London, where one of the Royal houses was

In Memory of Mr Peter Daniels

Born August 7, 1688. Died May 20, 1746.

Beneath this stone, a lump of clay,
Lies Uncle Peter Daniels,
Who too early in the month of May
Took off his winter flannels.

Medway, Massachusetts

Here Lies Fred

Here lies Fred
Who was alive and is dead.
Had it been his father,
I had much rather.
Had it been his brother,
Still better than another.
Had it been his sister,
No one would have missed her.
Had it been the whole generation,
Still better for the nation.
But since 'tis only Fred,
Who was alive, and is dead,
There's no more to be said.

Anon, c. 1751, on the death of Frederick, Prince of Wales, father of George III

A Woman to Her Lover

Do you come to me to bend me to your will
As conqueror to the vanquished
To make of me a bondslave
To bear you children, wearing out my life
In drudgery and silence
No servant will I be
If that be what you ask, O Lover I refuse you!

Or if you think to wed with one from heaven sent
Whose every deed and word and wish is golden
A wingless angel who can do no wrong
Go! - I am no doll to dress and sit for feeble worship
If that be what you ask, fool, I refuse you!

Or if you think in me to find
A creature who will have no greater joy
Than gratify your clamorous desire,
My skin soft only for your fond caresses
My body supple only for your sense delight,
Oh shame, and pity and abasement.
Not for you the hand of any wakened woman of our time.

But Lover, if you ask of me
That I shall be your comrade, friend, and mate,
To live and work, to love and die with you,
That so together we may know the purity and height
Of passion, and of joy and sorrow,
Then O husband, I am yours forever
And our co-equal love will make the stars to laugh with joy
And we shall have the music of the spheres for bridal march
And to its circling fugue[1] pass on, hand holding hand
Until we reach the very heart of God.

Christina Walsh, 1750-1800?

1. a complicated, harmonic piece of music, like a round

Midas's Touch

Midas, they say, possessed the art of old,
Of turning whatso'er he touch'd to gold;
This modern statesmen can reverse with ease;
Touch them with gold, they'll turn to what you please.

Sir John Byrom, c. 1760.

A Glazier's Verse

A
glazer I
Am and I
work for my
bred and many
fine window in my
time have I made
I with my dimond have
Cut out the Glass and
in a Corner Cist many
a prity lass 1789

On a window in the Plumbers' Arms, Skeldergate, York (the glazier inscribed his verse in a diamond, as here), 1789

Here Lie I

Underneath Lieth the Body of Robert Comonly Called Bone Phillip who died July 27th 1793 Aged 63 Years At whose request the following lines are here inserted

Here lie I at the Chancel door
Here lie I because I'm poor
The farther in the more you'll pay
Here lie I as warm as they.

From a tomb at Kingsbridge, Devon, 1793

Guinea Corn

This was probably a work song, sung somewhere in the Caribbean by African slaves. It would have been led by a gang-leader, calling out the lines, while everyone would chant 'Guinea Corn' at the moment of pulling on a chain, or lifting a load, or using a pick or axe. Work songs are the roots of blues, rhythm and blues, reggae, ragga, rap and rock'n' roll, which developed in America. In the Caribbean work songs were the beginnings of calypso, ska, rock-steady, reggae and combined with rap into ragga.

Guinea Corn[1], I long to see you
Guinea Corn, I long to plant you
Guinea Corn, I long to mould you
Guinea Corn, I long to weed you
Guinea Corn, I long to hoe you
Guinea Corn, I long to top you
Guinea Corn, I long to cut you
Guinea Corn, I long to dry you
Guinea Corn, I long to beat you
Guinea Corn, I long to trash[2] you
Guinea Corn, I long to parch[3] you
Guinea Corn, I long to grind you
Guinea Corn, I long to turn you
Guinea Corn, I long to eat you.

Work Song, Recorded 1797

1. a kind of millet
2. thresh, taking the husk off the corn by beating it with a flail
3. to dry

The Fate of Those Who Go for Soldiers

When into the Village or Town,
  A Recruiting the Soldiers do come;
With lies and with bullying around,
  They rattle away with the Drum;
When large sums of Money they promise,
  That they never intend for to pay,
But of this my brave fellows be certain
  You'll be shot at for Six-pence a day.
      Shot at for Six-pence a day.

With Thieves of all sorts they'll unite you,
  From the Gallows that's made their escape'
Your friends and relations will slight you,
  Then heart breaking sorrow's your fate;
With such wretches engage not to serve,
  Nor join in the Murderous lay;[1]
If you do you'll justly deserve,
  To be shot at for Six-pence a day.
      Shot at for Six-pence a day.

Then away to the Wars they will drag you,
  And victuals[2] you'll get when you call;
But war gives the Soldier in battle,
  A Breakfast of Powder and Ball.
Then should you be so foolishly bold,
  And advice you should throw far away;
You ne'er will live to grow old,
  When you're shot at for Six-pence a day.
      Shot at for Six-pence a day.

Then ne'er mind the sound of the drum,
  Stay at home with your sweethearts and
wives;
Free from harms to the Soldier that come,
  That lops off their limbs and their lives;

For the Captains will get all the Gold,
   And the Men lose their lives in the Fray;
Is not he a damned fool young or old,
   That is shot at for Six-pence a day?
            Shot at for Six-pence a day.

Sixty Thousand Englishmen have been
killed this last year in Holland. - Ten
Thousand more in the West Indies, and
Forty Thousand taken Prisoners. - Soldiers,
or Sailors, Death or Misery is your Portion.

Anon, 1797

1. song
2. food

For poor men recruitment usually meant being forced into joining up, either by their masters, or by being press-ganged by recruiting officers

The Volunteer

Dulce est pro patria mori[1]

When fivepence a solid meal cannot supply
To a jolly young man five feet ten inches high,
Who has jogged with his knapsack twelve leagues through
the rain,
While his wench and three brats had each ankle to strain,
The poor volunteer to the halberts[2] is tied,
For stealing two chick-eggs and getting them fried:
What carters and jockeys should suffer he feels,
And the blood gushes down from his nape to his heels.
The Commander-in-Chief, who is almost fifteen,
And a tailor's apprentice by right should have been,
Now struts round the circle, then turns on his heel
To belabour the drummers 'who don't make him feel'-
Swears England could ne'er have produced such a rogue,
And discerns in his howling the true Irish brogue.
The surgeon, whose sympathy swells in each vein,
When a swoon interrupts the convulsions of pain,
Makes them flog till he start to his senses again.
Nay, doctor and drum for attendance are paid,
And his pockets are fleeced while his shoulders are flayed.
He's packed in a transport on every state quarrel,
More tightly than biscuit and beef in a barrel;
In torrents each summer-shower streams through his tent,
In barracks more dismal December is spent;
In damp rotten bedding the moment he's laid,
To the rage of whole armies his rear is betrayed;
In health he infallibly more than half-starves,
In a fever he's used as a rascal deserves.
His Chloe, by hunger compelled to sad pranks,
Is chased as a swindler in form through the ranks;
His children, when some baggage-cart is o'erthrown,
In a ditch, like blind puppies, are suffered to drown.
And when for his King thirty years he has toiled,
In Canada frost-bit, in Africa broiled;

Has been thrice a week handcuffed for drinking his pay,
Got nine thousand lashes for running away;
Has oft like a hero been wounded *before*,
And cleared with a cudgel each concubine's score;
At last, with the Dons[3] point to point he engages,
For more than one-fourth of a scavenger's wages;
Some merciful volley then shatters a leg,
And his crutches procure him permission to beg.

Anon, 1791

1. Latin, meaning 'How sweet it is to die for one's country'
2. spear fitted with an axe head
3. Spanish soldiers

Supper is Na Ready

Roseberry to his lady says,
'My hinnie[1] and my succour,[2]
O shall we do the thing you ken[3]
Or shall we take our supper?'

Wi' modest face, sae fu' o'grace,
Replied the bonny lady;
'My noble lord do as you please
But supper is na ready.'

Robert Burns, c.1800

1. old Scottish dialect word for 'hen', still used nowadays to mean 'dear' or 'love'
2. help-mate
3. know

The Common and the Goose

The law locks up the man or woman
Who steals the goose from off the
common
But leaves the greater felon loose
Who steals the common from the goose.

Anon, c. 1800

The Pottery Worker

Beneath this stone lies Catherine Gray,
Changed to a lifeless lump of clay;
By earth and clay she got her pelf,[1]
And now she's changed to earth herself.
Ye weeping friends, let me advise,
Abate your tears and dry your eyes;
For what avails a flood of tears?
Who knows but in a course of years,
In some tall pitcher or brown pan,
She in her shop may be again.

In a churchyard in Chester. Catherine Gray was a pottery worker. 1750-1800?

1. money, wealth, property

The Twa Corbies[1]

As I was walking all alane,
I heard twa corbies making a mane;[2]
The tane unto the t'other say,
'Where sall we gang and dine to-day?'

'In behint yon auld fail dyke,[3]
I wot there lies a new slain knight;
And naebody kens[4] that he lies there,
But his hawk, his hound, and lady fair.

'His hound is to the hunting gane,
His hawk to fetch the wild-fowl hame,
His lady's ta'en another mate,
So we may mak our dinner sweet.

Ye'll sit on his white hause-bane,[5]
And I'll pike out his bonny blue een;[6]
Wi ae[7] lock o his gowden hair
We'll theek[8] our nest when it grows bare.

'Mony a one for him makes mane,
But nane sall ken where he is gane;
Oer his white banes, when they are bare,
The wind sall blaw for evermair.

Traditional song, recorded 1803

1. Scots name for a raven or crow
2. moaning
3. turf wall
4. knows
5. neck-bone
6. eyes
7. one
8. thatch

GREEN.

What Is Slavery?[1]

This poem was written after Shelley heard that 13 people had been killed at a meeting of workers and their families asking for reform of the voting system in St. Peter's Fields, Manchester. The armed police, recruited by the local landlords and gentry, charged the crowd. When Shelley wrote the poem it was too dangerous to publish it and it was only published in 1832, after his death.

XL

'Tis to work and have such pay
As just keeps life from day to day
In your limbs, as in a cell
For the tyrants' use to dwell,

XLI

'So that ye for them are made
Loom, and plough, and sword, and spade,
With or without your own will bent
To their defence and nourishment.

XLII

'Tis to see your children weak
With their mothers pine and peak,
When the winter winds are bleak, -
They are dying whilst I speak.

XLIII

'Tis to hunger for such diet
As the rich man in his riot
Casts to the fat dogs that lie
Surfeiting[2] beneath his eye;

XLIV

'Tis to let the Ghost of God
Take from Toil a thousandfold
More than e'er its substance could
In the tyrannies of old.[3]

Percy Bysshe Shelley, from 'The Mask of Anarchy', 1819

1. slavery here means the slavery of workers in England at the time of the Industrial Revolution
2. having too much of something
3. even in Biblical times, tyrants did not make as much profit from workers as religious people in Shelley's time make from enslaving workers

The Factory Girl's Last Day

'Twas on a winter's morning,
The weather wet and wild,
Three hours before the dawning
The father roused his child;
Her daily morsel bringing,
The darksome room he paced,
And cried, 'The bell is ringing,
My hapless darling, haste!'

'Father, I'm up, but weary,
I scarce can reach the door,
And long the way and dreary, —
O carry me once more!
To help us we've no mother;
And you have no employ;
They killed my little brother,—
Like him I'll work and die!'

Her wasted form seemed nothing,—
The load was at his heart;
The sufferer he kept soothing
Till at the mill they part.
The overlooker met her,
As to her frame she crept,
And with his thong he beat her,
And cursed her as she wept.

Alas! what hours of horror
Made up her latest day;
In toil, and pain, and sorrow,
They slowly passed away:
It seemed, as she grew weaker,
The threads the oftener broke,
The rapid wheels ran quicker,
And heavier fell the stroke.

The sun had long descended
But night brought no repose;
Her day began and ended
As cruel tyrants chose.
At length a little neighbour
Her halfpenny she paid
To take her last hour's labour,
While by her frame she laid.

At last, the engine ceasing,
The captives homeward rushed;
She thought her strength increasing —
'Twas hope her spirits flushed:
She left, but oft she tarried,
She fell and rose no more,
Till, by her comrades carried,
She reached her father's door.

All night, with tortured feeling,
He watched his speechless child;
While, close beside her kneeling,
She knew him not, nor smiled.
Again the factory's ringing
Her last perceptions tried;
When, from her straw-bed springing,
'Tis time!' she shrieked, and died!

That night a chariot passed her,
While on the ground she lay;
The daughters of her master
An evening visit pay:
Their tender hearts were sighing
As negro wrongs were told,—
While the white slave lay dying,
Who earned their father's gold!

Michael Thomas Sadler, c.1820

Epitaph to Castlereagh

Posterity will ne'er survey
A nobler grave than this:
Here lie the bones of Castlereagh:[1]
Stop, traveller, and piss.

George Gordon, Lord Byron, 1821

1. a much-hated minister, satirised in the cartoon below, taken from a newspaper of the time

Ah Sidney!

The wedding day decided was,
The wedding wine provided;
But ere the day did come along
He drunk it up and died did.
 Ah Sidney! Ah Sidney!

Sidney Snyder died1823, aged 20
Providence, Rhode Island

The Foddering Boy

The foddering boy along the crumping[1] snows
With straw-band-belted legs and folded arm
Hastens, and on the blast that keenly blows
Oft turns for breath, and beats his fingers warm,
And shakes the lodging snow from off his
clothes,
Buttoning his doublet closer from the storm
And slouching his brown beaver[2] o'er his nose -
Then faces it agen, and seeks the stack
Within its circling fence where hungry lows
Expecting cattle, making many a track
About the snow, impatient for the sound
When in huge forkfuls trailing at his back
He litters the sweet hay about the ground
And brawls to call the staring cattle round.

John Clare c.1830

1. brittle
2. hat

John Clare was the son of an agricultural worker, living some of the time on poor relief. He lived in Northamptonshire and worked as a thresher, farm labourer and gardener. As a boy he watched the enclosure of the land by the gentry, preventing the local people from being able to graze their animals on what was previously common land.

The Engineer's Epitaph

My engine now is cold and still
No water does my boiler fill
My coke affords its flames no more
My days of usefulness are o'er
My wheels deny their noted speed
No more my guiding hands they heed
My whistle too has lost its tone
Its shrill and thrilling sounds are gone
My valves are now thrown open wide
My flanges[1] now refuse to guide
My clacks,[2] also, though once so strong
Refuse to aid the busy throng
No more I feel each urging breath
My steam is now condensed in death
Life's railway's o'er, each station's past
In death I'm stopp'd and rest at last
Farewell dear friends and cease to weep
In Christ I'm safe, in Him I sleep.

Epitaph for a railway worker in a Bromsgrove churchyard, Worcester, 1840

1. a raised rim
2. part of the pump, which made a clacking sound

The Fine, Old English Gentleman

TO BE SAID OR SUNG AT ALL CONSERVATIVE DINNERS

I'll sing you a new ballad, and I'll warrant it's first-rate,
Of the days of that old gentleman who had that old estate;
When they spent the public money at a bountiful old rate
On ev'ry mistress, pimp, and scamp, at ev'ry noble gate,
 In the fine old English Tory times;
 Soon may they come again!

The good old laws were garnished well with gibbets,[1] whips, and chains,
With fine old English penalties, and fine old English pains,
With rebel heads, and seas of blood once hot in rebel veins;
For all these things were requisite to guard the rich old gains
 Of the fine old English Tory times;
 Soon may they come again!

This brave old code, like Argus,[2] had a hundred watchful eyes,
And ev'ry English peasant had his good old English spies,
To tempt his starving discontent with fine old English lies,
Then call the good old Yeomanry[3] to stop his peevish cries,
 In the fine old English Tory times;
 Soon may they come again!

The good old times for cutting throats that cried out in their need,
The good old times for hunting men who held their fathers' creed,
The good old times when William Pitt,[4] as all good men agreed,
Came down direct from Paradise at more than railroad speed ...
 Oh the fine old English Tory times;
 When will they come again!

In those rare days, the press was seldom known to snarl or bark,
But sweetly sang of men in pow'r, like any tuneful lark;
Grave judges, too, to all their evil deeds were in the dark;
And not a man in twenty score knew how to make his mark.
 Oh the fine old English Tory times;
 Soon may they come again!

Those were the days for taxes, and for war's infernal din;
For scarcity of bread, that fine old dowagers[5] might win;
For shutting men of letters[6] up, through iron bars to grin,
Because they didn't think the Prince was altogether thin,
In the fine old English Tory times;
Soon may they come again!

But Tolerance, though slow in flight, is strong-wing'd in the main;
That might must come on these fine days, in course of time was plain;
The pure old spirit struggled, but its struggles were in vain;
A nation's grip was on it, and it died in choking pain,
With the fine old English Tory days,
All of the olden time.

The bright old day now dawns again; the cry runs through the land,
In England there shall be dear bread - in Ireland, sword and brand,
And poverty, and ignorance, shall swell the rich and grand,
So, rally round the rulers with the gentle iron hand,
Of the fine old English Tory days;
Hail to the coming time!

Charles Dickens, 1841

1. hanging posts
2. a figure from Greek mythology, with a hundred eyes, only two of which slept at any one time.
3. an army of freemen and farmers
4. the Prime Minister from the 'fine old Tory times'
5. widows who have inherited money
6. educated men

No!

No sun—no moon!
No morn—no noon—
No dawn—no dusk—no proper time of day—
No sky—no earthly view—
No distance looking blue—
No road—no street—no 't'other side the way'—
No end to any Row—
No indications where the Crescents go—
No top to any steeple—
No recognitions of familiar people—
No courtesies for showing 'em—
No knowing 'em!—
No travelling at all—no locomotion,
No inkling of the way—no notion—
'No go'—by land or ocean—
No mail—no post—
No news from any foreign coast—
No Park—no Ring—no afternoon gentility—
No company—no nobility,—
No warmth, no cheerfulness, no healthful ease,
No comfortable feel in any member—
No shade, no shine, no butterflies, no bees,
No fruits, no flowers, no leaves, no birds,
November!

Thomas Hood, 1844

The Recruited Collier

Oh, what's the matter wi' you, my lass,
An' where's your dashin' Jimmy?
The sowdger boys have picked him up
And sent him far, far frae me.

Last pay-day he set off to town,
And them red-coated fellows
Enticed him in and made him drunk,
And he'd better gone to the gallows.

The very sight o' his cockade,[1]
It set us all a-crying;
And me, I fairly fainted twice,
I thought that I was dyin.

My father would have paid the smart,[2]
And run for the golden guinea,
But the sergeant swore he'd kissed the book,
And now they've got young Jimmy.

When Jimmy talks about the wars
It's worse than death to hear him.
I must go out and hide my tears,
Because I cannot bear him.

For aye he jibes and cracks his jokes,
And bids me not forsake him.
A brigadier or grenadier,
He says they're sure to make him.

As I walked over the stubble field,
Below it runs the seam,[3]
I thought o' Jimmy hewin there,
But it was all a dream.

He hewed the very coals we burn,
And when the fire I'se leetin,[4]
To think the lumps was in his hands,
It sets my heart to beatin.

So break my heart, and then it's ower,
So break my heart, my dearie,
And I'll lie in the cold, cold grave,
For of single life I'm weary.

Anon, c. 1850

1. a ribbon worn in your hat if you had been called up or were in the army
2. a sum of money you had to pay to be discharged from the army
3. a seam of coal
4. I was lighting

Monster Science

A Lord of Steam and Iron am I,
A Monster in the land;
While puny men of bone and blood
Are slaves at my command.

The Monster Science is my name
And I trample on the free,
I laugh at the sight of human tears
And Death is my Victory.

I love the knell of the factory bell
On the long dark winter night,
With hail and storms and shivering forms
Who toil by candlelight.

Of Iron and Steam I reign supreme
But a partial[1] King am I
The few by stealth I heap with wealth
While the masses sicken and die.

Anon, c.1850

1. taking sides

The Slave Mother

The poet was an African American woman, born of free parents, who campaigned for the abolition of slavery in America.

Heard you that shriek? It rose
So wildly on the air,
It seem'd as if a burden'd heart
Was breaking in despair.

Saw you those hands so sadly clasped—
The bowed and feeble head—
The shuddering of that fragile form—
That look of grief and dread?

Saw you the sad, imploring eye?
Its every glance was pain,
As if a storm of agony
Were sweeping through the brain.

She is a mother pale with fear,
Her boy clings to her side,
And in her kyrtle[1] vainly tries
His trembling form to hide.

He is not hers, although she bore
For him a mother's pains;
He is not hers, although her blood
Is coursing through his veins!

He is not hers, for cruel hands
May rudely tear apart
The only wreath of household love
That binds her breaking heart.

His love has been a joyous light
That o'er her pathway smiled,
A fountain gushing ever new,
Amid life's desert wild.

His lightest word has been a tone
Of music round her heart,
Their lives a streamlet blent in one—
Oh, Father! must they part?

They tear him from her circling arms,
Her last and fond embrace:—
Oh! never more may her sad eyes
Gaze on his mournful face.

No marvel, then, those bitter shrieks
Disturb the listening air;
She is a mother, and her heart
Is breaking in despair.

Frances Ellen Watkins Harper, 1854

1. skirt

We Raise The Wheat

We raise the wheat,
They give us the corn,
We sift the meal,
They give us the husk,
We peel the meat,
They give us the skin,
And that's the way they take us in.

Slave song, c.1855

What I Know Is Me

Got one mind for the boss to see,
Got another mind for what I know is me.

Anonymous slave, USA, c. 1860

My Lord Tomnoddy

My Lord Tomnoddy's the son of an Earl,
His hair is straight, but his whiskers curl;
His Lordship's forehead is far from wide,
But there's plenty of room for the brains inside.
He writes his name with indifferent ease,
He's rather uncertain about the 'd's, -
But what does it matter, if three or one,
To the Earl of Fitzdotterel's eldest son?

My Lord Tomnoddy to college went,
Much time he lost, much money he spent;
Rules, and windows, and heads, he broke -
Authorities wink'd - young men will joke!
He never peep'd inside of a book -
In two year's time a degree he took;
And the newspapers vaunted the honours won
By the Earl of Fitzdotterel's eldest son.

My Lord Tomnoddy came out in the world,
Waists were tighten'd, and ringlets curl'd.
Virgins languished, and matrons smil'd -
'Tis true, his Lordship is rather wild;
In very queer places he spends his life;
There's talk of some children, by nobody's wife -
But we mustn't look close into what is done
By the Earl of Fitzdotterel's eldest son.

My Lord Tomnoddy must settle down -
There's a vacant seat[1] in the family town!
('Tis time he should sow his eccentric oats) -
He hasn't the wit to apply for votes:
He cannot e'en learn his election speech,
Three phrases he speaks - a mistake in each!
And then breaks down - but the borough[2] is won
For the Earl of Fitzdotterel's eldest son.

My Lord Tomnoddy prefers the Guards,
(The House is a bore) so! - it's on the cards!
My Lord's a Lieutenant at twenty-three,
A Captain at twenty-six is he -
He never drew sword, except on drill;
The tricks of parade he has learnt but ill -
A full-blown Colonel at thirty-one
Is the Earl of Fitzdotterel's eldest son!

My Lord Tomnoddy is thirty-four;
The Earl can last but a few years more.
My Lord in the Peers will take his place:
Her Majesty's councils his words will grace.
Office he'll hold, and patronage sway;
Fortunes and lives he will vote away -
And what are his qualifications? - ONE!
He's the Earl of Fitzdotterel's eldest son.

Robert Barnabas Brough, 1859

1. a parliamentary seat where the MP has died or resigned, so Tomnoddy can go for it.
2. the parliamentary constituency

The Factory Bell

Come, Billy, come; dos yer[1] yon bell?
Thou'll ha' yon mill agate
Afore thou'rt up![2] Do stir thisel'
Or else thou'll be too late:
I know thou'rt tire't, my lad - I know;
What can a body do?
It's very cowd; but, frost or snow,
Thou knows thou'll ha' to goo!

An' th' north woint's blowin' keen an' shrill;
It's bin a stormy neet;
Thou'll ha' to run o' the' gate to th' mill;
It's thick wi' drivin' sleet;
There's not a candle lef i' th' house;
Thou'll don thisel'[3] i' th' dark;
Come, come my lad; jump up at once,
An' hie tho to thi wark!

I can hardly keep up on my feet;
I'm full o' aches and pains;
An' I's ha' to wesh from morn to neet,[4]
For very little gains.
It looks hard fortin' for us both,
But it's what we han to dree;[5]
We mun do as weel's we con, my lad;
There's nobbut thee an' me!

Come, come; I have thi stockin's here,
An' thi breeches, an' thi shoon;
Thou'll find thi jacket on yon cheer;
An' thi dinner's upo' th' oon.[6]
I'll lock yon dur, an I'll tak' th' keigh;
I think we's find o' reet;
So manage th' best thou con, my lad,
Till I come whoam at neet!

Then not another word wur said;
But Billy, like a mon,
Geet up out of his little bed,
An' poo'd his stockin's on;
An' off he went, through sleet and snow,
With his dinner in a can;
He'd a bit o' oon-cake[7] in his mouth,
An' he donned him as he ran.[8]

Some folk can lie till th' clock strikes eight;
Some folk may sleep till ten,
Then rub their e'en an' yawn a bit,
An' turn 'em o'er again;
Some folk can ring a bell i' bed,
Till th' sarvant brings some tay;
But weet or dry, a factory lad
Mun jump at break o' day!

Edwin Waugh, c.1860

1. hear
2. the mill will have started up before you have got up.
3. you'll fall down
4. And I have to wash from morning to night
5. suffer
6. oven
7. oven-cake
8. and he downed it as he ran

Two Strings to a Bow

I don't want the one that I don't want to know
  That I want the one that I want:
But the one that I want now wants me to go
  And give up the one I don't want.
Why I don't want the one that I don't want to know
  That I want the one that I want,
Is if I miss the one that I want (don't you know)
  I might want the one I don't want.

Anon, c.1880

Is it Fair?

The rain it raineth on the just
And also on the unjust fella
But chiefly on the just, because
The unjust steals the just's umbrella.

Charles, Baron Bowen, c.1880

The Greatest Bore

The greatest bore is boredom,
  The greatest nuisance known
Is he who talks about himself
  And *his* affairs alone,
When you want *him* to listen
  While you talk about your own.

Anon, re-printed from Fun Magazine, 1885

Some English Prisons

Millbank for thick shins and graft at the pump;
Broadmoor for all laggs[1] as go off their chump;
Brixton for good toke[2] and cocoa with fat;
Dartmoor for bad grub but plenty of chat;
Portsmouth a blooming bad place for hard work;
Chatham on Sunday give four ounce of pork;
Portland is worst of the lot for to joke in -
For fetching a lagging[3] there's no place like
Woking.

Anon, 1885, scratched with a nail onto the bottom of a dinner-can at Millbank prison

1. convicts
2. bread
3. doing a sentence in prison

A London Fete

All night fell hammers, shock on shock;
With echoes Newgate's[1] granite clanged:
The scaffold built, at eight o'clock
They brought the man out to be hanged.
Then came from all the people there
A single cry, that shook the air;
Mothers held up their babes to see,
Who spread their hands, and crowed with glee;
Here a girl from her vesture tore
A rag to wave with, and joined the roar;
There a man, with yelling tired,
Stopped, and the culprit's crime inquired;
A sot,[2] below the doomed man dumb,
Bawled his health in the world to come;
These blasphemed and fought for places;
These, half-crushed, with frantic faces,
To windows, where, in freedom sweet,
Others enjoyed the wicked treat.
At last, the show's black crisis pended;
Struggles for better standings ended;
The rabble's lips no longer cursed,
But stood agape with horrid thirst;
Thousands of breasts beat horrid hope;
Thousands of eyeballs, lit with hell,
Burnt one way all, to see the rope
Unslacken as the platform fell.
The rope flew tight; and then the roar
Burst forth afresh; less loud, but more
Confused and affrighting than before.
A few harsh tongues for ever led
The common din, the chaos of noises,
But ear could not catch what they said.
As when the realm of the damned rejoices

At winning a soul to its will,
That clatter and clangour of hateful voices
Sickened and stunned the air, until
The dangling corpse hung straight and still.
The show complete, the pleasure past,
The solid masses loosened fast:
A thief slunk off, with ample spoil,
To ply elsewhere his daily toil;
A baby strung its doll to a stick;
A mother praised the pretty trick;
Two children caught and hanged a cat;
Two friends walked on, in lively chat;
And two, who had disputed places,
Went forth to fight, with murderous faces.

Coventry Patmore, 1890

1. London prison and death-row
2. drunkard

Cork and Work and Card and Ward

I take it you already know
Of tough and bough and cough and dough?
Others may stumble, but not you
On hiccough, thorough, laugh, and through?
I write in case you wish perhaps
To learn of less familiar traps:
Beware of heard, a dreadful word
That looks like beard, and sounds like bird.
And dead: it's said like bed, not bead;
For goodness' sake, don't call it 'deed'!
Watch out for meat and great and threat
(They rhyme with suite and straight and debt).
A moth is not a moth in mother,
Nor both in bother, broth in brother.
And here is not a match for there,
Nor dear for bear, or fear for pear.
There's dose and rose, there's also lose
(Just look them up), and goose, and choose,
And cork and work, and card and ward,
And font and front, and word and sword,
And do and go and thwart and cart -
Come come, I've barely made a start!
A dreadful language? Man alive,
I'd mastered it when I was five!

Anon, c. 1900

Fight? What For?

I am 'wanted to go in the army.'
Well, what would they give me to do?
'You'll have to be killing your brothers
If one of them doesn't kill you.'

I am 'wanted to go in the army.'
Say, what is there in it for me?
'You'd help to be saving your country
From brother-men over the sea.'

My country? Who says I've a country?
I live in another man's flat
That hasn't as much as a door yard -
And why should I battle for that?

I haven't a lot nor a building,
No flower, no garden, nor tree.
The landlords have gobbled the country -
Let *them* do the fighting, not me.

Celia Whitehead, c .1900

John Bun

Here lies John Bun,
He was killed by a gun,
His name was not Bun, but Wood,
But Wood would not rhyme with gun, but
Bun would.

Anon, date unknown

The Death of Queen Jane

Queen Jane lay in labour full nine days or more,
Till the women were so tired, they could stay no longer there,

'Good women, good women, good women as ye be,
Do open my right side, and find my baby.'

'Oh no,' said the women. 'That never may be,
We will send for King Henry, and hear what he say.'

King Henry was sent for, King Henry did come:
'What do ail you, my lady, your eyes look so dim?'

'King Henry, King Henry, will you do one thing for me?
That's to open my right side, and find my baby.'

'Oh, no,' said King Henry. 'That's a thing I'll never do.
If I lose the flower of England, I shall lose the branch too.'

King Henry went mourning, and so did his men,
And so did the dear baby, for Queen Jane did die then.

And how deep was the mourning, how black were the bands,
How yellow, yellow were the flamboys they carried in their
hands.

There was fiddling, aye, and dancing on the day the babe was
born
But poor Queen Jane beloved lay cold as a stone.

A folk song, recorded in 1907

Activities Section

Activities on Individual Poems

An Anglo-Saxon Riddle (page 6)

1. Look at the word-for-word translation of the riddle on Page 6. Talk about what you think the answer to the riddle is. If you can't work it out yet, don't worry. The answer is coming up soon!

2. See if you can match the words of the translation to the Anglo-Saxon words by writing them in under the Anglo-Saxon version. Make a list of all of the things you notice about what's interesting or different about Anglo-Saxon English. e.g. What's different about the word order? Which letters are different?

3. Here are three different modern English translations of the Anglo-Saxon riddle. One of them gives you the answer to the riddle.

Read all three of them aloud more than once.
On the basis of these first readings, which translation do you like best?
Is the reason for your choice:

- the sounds of the words?
- whether it gives you the answer to the riddle or not?
- particular lines or phrases that you especially enjoy listening to or reading?
- whether it sounds modern or not?
- whether it uses interesting words?
- whether it is simple or complicated?

A moth ate words.
When I heard of that wonder
I thought it was an amazing happening
that a worm, a thief in the darkness
has swallowed a man's song
a great saying and a strong foundation.
The stealing visitor was not one jot the wiser
when he swallowed the words.
What am I?
Answer: a book-worm

Michael Rosen

A moth, I thought, munching a word.
How marvellously weird!
Digesting a man's sayings-
A sneakthief nibbling in the shadows
At the shape of a poet's thunderous phrases-
How unutterably strange!
And the pilfering parasite none the wiser
For the words he has swallowed.

Gerard Benson

A moth ate words; a marvellous event
I thought it when I heard about that wonder,
A worm had swallowed some man's lay, a thief
In darkness had consumed the mighty saying
With its foundation firm. The thief was not
One whit the wiser when he ate those words.

Richard Hamer

Ideas for Writing

1. Try writing your own translation of the poem. You can be a steal-guest/thief/sneakthief and take words and phrases from any of the translations as well as using your own words. For instance, if you like Benson's phrase, 'munching a word', you could use that but choose Hamer's 'a worm has swallowed'.

Read each other's poems aloud to each other and put them up on the wall to allow you to compare the different versions.

2. Write your own Riddle poem, in which you give clues about what you are writing about and leave it to the reader to work out what you are describing.

Read each others Riddles and see if you can work out the answers to them.

The Covetous Man (page 10)

1. A covetous person is always wanting to possess things that belong to other people, whether it's their money or their possessions or their husband or wife. Covetousness is one of the Seven Deadly Sins. Langland turns covetousness into a person. He shows his disapproval of covetousness by making the person physically repulsive.
Look at the representations of the Seven Deadly Sins on Page 98. See if you can work out which is which. Which one is missing?

Take one of the other Seven Deadly Sins and turn it into a person.

Anger	Avarice	Envy
Gluttony	Lust	Pride
Sloth		

Make a list of all the physical characteristics and behaviour you might associate with that Sin. e.g. Gluttony: fat, holding a big packet of chips wrapped in newspaper, saliva dribbling down his/her mouth, nose pressed up against the window of a bakery etc.
Write a poem about the person, starting 'And along came Gluttony'

2. Langland gave his poetry a rhythm by repeating the first letter sounds in each line. When he was writing in the 14th Century, this was a very common style. It was called alliterative verse. Say the poem out loud, stopping after each line. For each line, try to work out which first letter sounds are repeated e.g. b is the sound in 'He was so bitelbrowed and baberlipped also.'

Take one or two of the lines of your poem and try to turn it into alliterative verse. If it works well, you could re-draft the whole of your poem using alliteration.

The Schoolboy (page 16)

1. Read through the poem once to get the general gist of it. Talk about it, trying to work out what the difficult bits mean, using the notes on the page to help you. What kind of boy is the schoolboy? What's his attitude to school? Which bits of his description of going to school do you especially like? Which of the things he talks about have you felt yourself?

2. Try writing a 'loose' modern translation of the poem, updating it and making it seem like a modern school child speaking.

You could think about which bits of the original poem would have been schoolboy slang in his day. For instance, grown-ups might have 'peppered his arse' for saying, 'pepered my ars'! How might you translate that into modern, 'naughty' English?

Also, think about the images and comparisons he uses when he wishes the worst fate for his master. What do they suggest about where he lives, what he sees happening around him in terms of work, the environment and what he probably does in his own spare time? Use images and comparisons drawn from a modern school pupil's life and environment. For instance, you wouldn't say 'I wish my master were a hare.' What might you say instead?

3. Read each others translations of the poem.

The Passionate Shepherd to His Love and Other Versions (page 22)

Christopher Marlowe wrote 'The Passionate Shepherd to this Love' in 1600. 'The Nymph's Reply to the Shepherd' on Page 23 was a response to the poem written by Sir Walter Raleigh. A later poem, 'The Wooing Rogue', on Page 31, is also using Marlowe's poem and doing something a bit different with it.

1. Read all three poems more than once.

2. Make a chart, which allows you to compare the three poems, what attitudes to love they are expressing and what kind of language they use.
Your chart could include columns with the following titles:

What Images?
What Landscape?
Who's the Poem Speaking to?
Who is the Speaker?
What's the Attitude of the Speaker to Love?
What's the Attitude of the Poet to Love?

3. List the features of the original poem that have been kept in each of the new versions. Why do you think the poets chose to keep parts of the original poem? What happens to those parts of the poem when they appear in the new versions?

4. Do you think you would have to have read 'The Passionate Shepherd to his Love' to enjoy and understand the other poems?

Ideas for Writing

1. Write a comparison between 'The Passionate Shepherd to His Love' and the other versions, using your chart to help you explore what the poems say about love, what changes have been made to the original poem and what the effect of these changes is.

2. 'The Passionate Shepherd to His Love' has been 're-told' by poets wanting to write about love across the centuries. It's almost as if poets have it in their heads as a model of a particular kind of love poetry. They can make their own statement by using it as a starting-point but adapt it for a different society and a different set of attitudes and challenge the ways in which love is described as well.
Here is one modern version by C. Day Lewis:

Come live with me and be my love,
And we will all the pleasures prove
Of peace and plenty; bed and board,
That chance employment may afford.

I'll handle dainties on the docks
And thou shalt read of summer frocks;
At evening by the sour canals
We'll hope to hear some madrigals.

Care on thy maiden brow shall put
A wreath of wrinkles, and thy foot
Be shod with pain, not silken dress
But toil shall tire they loveliness.

Hunger shall make thy modest zone
And cheat fond death of all but bone -
If these delights thy mind may move,
Then live with me and be my love.

C. Day Lewis (1904-1972)

Try doing your own version of the poem. First experiment on the first few verses to see what difference a few changes might make. Treat these experiments as rough drafts that you will choose bits from when you write a final version.
Try:

- changing the speaker to a woman talking to a man;
- doing it as a dialogue, with one verse being the woman, the other the man replying to her;
- up-dating the language in some way, either into modern Standard English, or a dialect (like cockney, Yorkshire or patois), or into a style of speech (like rap, or BBC News Broadcast English, or Blind Date style);
- writing it from a different point of view, such as someone who is a single parent, or recently divorced, or about to enter an arranged marriage, or in love with an unattainable pop or film star, or someone who has just fallen out of love.

Now take the bits of your experiments that you liked and turn them into a whole poem. While you are writing you should be thinking about what you want your poem to say about love and how you want to adapt the original to fit your experience and the attitudes and values of your society.

To the Ladies (page 44)

1. 'That wretched state'

'that fatal knot'

Talk about what you think these phrases might be referring to?

2. Some words have been left out of the beginning of this poem. Try to see if you can put in words of your own that would make sense in the context.

To the ....

...........and servant are the same
But only differ in the name:
For when that fatal knot is tied,
Which nothing, nothing can divide,
When she the word.........has said,
And..........by law supreme is made,
Then all that's kind is laid aside,
And nothing left but state and pride.

3. Read the whole poem. In one sentence, try to say what Mary, Lady Chudleigh's advice is to women.
She wrote the poem in the seventeenth century. What might the reaction have been? From a female reader? From a male reader?
How do we read it differently? Could a similar poem be written today?
Write a letter to Lady Chudleigh, from a female reader or a male reader at the time.

Women, Sex and Marriage

1. Another poem in the anthology, 'A Woman to Her Lover', written between fifty and one hundred years later, also explores a woman's feelings about her relationship with a man. Read this poem. Make a chart comparing the two poems. Talk and write about the similarities and differences between them.

2. Read some of the other poems about women's relationships with men, which are listed below:

A Betrayed Maiden's Lament
A Servant Girl's Holiday
The Death of Queen Jane (1) and (2)
Song: The Willing Mistress
A Beautiful Young Nymph Going to Bed
Supper is Na Ready

How would you describe the attitude of the women towards men, sex, marriage and having babies?

Note down the dates of the poems. Does knowing the date make any difference to the way you read the poem?

Look at the name of the poet. Does knowing the gender of the poet make any difference to the way you read the poem?

Try to make a visual chart or diagram to show some of the issues and themes raised in these poems and how the ideas expressed seem to you to have changed over time. You could include a timeline as part of your diagram.

A Beautiful Young Nymph Going to Bed (page 47)

1. Talk about what these words and phrases make you think of and what sort of poem they might come from.

> nymph
> tresses
> a beautiful young nymph going to bed
> her bower
> the lovely goddess
> With gentlest touch
> Corinna, pride of.......
> Corinna wakes
> shepherd sighs in vain
> at the midnight hour
> Behold

Try writing a quick draft of a poem with the title, 'A Beautiful Young Nymph Going to Bed', using all of the words and phrases listed above somewhere in your poem and linking them with your own words. Read the poems aloud to each other.

2. Jonathan Swift's poem starts,

> Corinna, pride of Drury Lane,
> For whom no shepherd sighs in vain;

Talk about what you expect of the poem now that you have read the first two lines.

3. Read the whole poem aloud.
Talk about what you expected the poem to be like and what you now think of it. What has changed?

4. Go through the poem finding words and phrases which contrast with the list of words and phrases you were given before reading the whole poem. Make two columns, one with all of the words given to you before reading the poem, the other with the contrasting words. Think of a title for each of the two lists, which says something about what kinds of words they are.

5. At what point in the poem were your expectations challenged? Mark the first point at which you began to doubt what kind of nymph Corinna was.

6. What do you think the attitude of the narrator is to Corinna? Find evidence in the poem to support each of these views and set out your evidence in two columns:

He is sympathetic to her	He is disgusted by her

Corinna Answers Back

If Corinna had read this poem, what would she have wanted to say? One person should read the poem aloud, pausing after every two lines to allow Corinna to reply. The rest of the group can take it in turns to give Corinna's view.

> e.g. Corinna, pride of Drury Lane,
> For whom no shepherd sighs in vain;

' It's not my fault that no-one loves me. I was loved once but he left me without a penny to my name, so I was forced to get money whatever way I could. Love-sick shepherds are all very well but they don't pay the bills, do they? '

The Purpose of the Poem

Talk about this list of statements and decide which one best expresses your view:

- Swift is trying to show how cruel society can be to women.
- Swift is condemning women who turn to prostitution.
- Swift wants to sympathise with Corinna but finds her too revolting to be sympathetic.
- Swift wants us to laugh when we read the poem.
- Swift wants to shock us into taking a social issue seriously.
- Swift is anti-women.
- There are all kinds of contradictory things going on in this poem.

The Foddering Boy (page 69)

Bringing the Foddering Boy to Life

1. Work in pairs. You are going to prepare a reading of the poem, in which one of you acts out the part of the foddering boy, whilst the other reads the poem aloud. Talk through the poem and annotate it, marking down what the boy's actions will be at different stages in the poem. Perform your dramatisation for another pair, or for the whole class.

2. What is the foddering boy thinking about? Read the poem aloud, stopping at the end of each line. Write in thought bubbles on your poem at several different stages in the poem.

> e.g. The cows will be expecting me. Cold as I am, they have to be fed.
> But why's it got to be me?

What Does It Do for Me?

Which of these statements do you agree with most?

- The poem creates a strong picture of a scene.
- The poem makes the reader feel the cold.
- The sound of the words is enjoyable - it's fun to read aloud.
- This poem doesn't do anything for me.
- The poem gives an interesting view of child labour in the nineteenth century.

A Modern Foddering Boy?

Try writing your own modern version of 'The Foddering Boy' e.g.

The Newspaper Boy/Girl
The Part-time Supermarket Shelf Filler
The Baby-sitter
The Car Windscreen Washer Who Waits for Business at Traffic Lights
The Seller of Roses by the Roadside

The Engineer's Epitaph (page 70)

In this poem written on a tombstone, the railwayman's dead body is compared to the steam engine that he used to drive.

The author of the poem used his sense of fun to imagine that the steam engine had a life of its own. Can you relate any parts of the engine to a part of the human body?

Try writing an epitaph for a modern day worker that uses a similar device. It doesn't have to be long. Here are some suggestions:

- Computer operator
- Cyclist
- Lorry Driver
- Photographer
- Guitarist
- Nurse
- Teacher.

Start by making a list of all of the tools of the job, or all of the parts of the machinery or equipment used. Choose one of these and experiment with writing a first line that links it to the person's life.

For instance, for a computer operator, who died of a sudden illness, the first line might be:

My disk's been wiped and I had no back up

A guitarist's epitaph might start:

My strings are broken, my plectrum cracked,

Continue by using the other items on your list.
Try reading the finished poems aloud to each other, without saying whose epitaph it is and see whether other people can work out what job the worker did.

Two Poems on the Death of Queen Jane (pages 18 & 92)

1. Read aloud the two versions of the death of one of Henry VIII's wives. They both narrate the same event but with some important differences.

2. In small groups, re-read the poems carefully and pick out any differences in the telling of the story. Think about:

- differences in the attitude of the narrator to King Henry VIII and Queen Jane;
- whether any details are left out in one of the versions;
- whether any details of the event are emphasised in either version;
- whether the tone of one version is more emotional or more distanced than the other.

Discuss why you think 300 years might make a difference to the way an historical event looks.

Ideas for Writing

1. Using your understanding of the two versions, write two short imaginative pieces:

> Henry VIII's official court press release the day after Queen Jane's death.
>
> Three journal entries by one of the midwives covering the labour, birth and death.

2. Choose one newsworthy event. It could be from the current news or an important event in recent history that interests you, for instance the death of a famous person, like John Lennon or John F. Kennedy. It could be a political event, like the downfall of Margaret Thatcher or an event of national concern, such as the Hillsborough Stadium disaster or the bomb on the Pan Am airliner over Lockerbie.

Try writing a narrative poem about the event. You will need to think carefully about what view of the event you want to put across, what details to include and what your main purpose is in telling the story of the event. Is it to tell an exciting story, or to blame someone for the events, or to make your audience feel as if they were there, or to make your audience feel saddened by what happened?

'Clever Tom Clinch Going to be Hanged' and 'A London Fete' (pages 45 & 88)

1. Read each of these poems in turn, if possible on photocopied sheets.
Read them a second time, this time using a pencil to underline and make notes around the poems.

- Underline any words or phrases that suggest the poet's attitude towards hanging.
- Put a circle around any words or phrases which show the effects a public hanging has on the people in the crowd.
- In a different colour, underline any words or phrases that especially helped you to imagine the scene. Which of these things do they convey: the way things looked, the smells, the sounds, the feelings of people?
- Look at whose eyes the events are seen through. Is it through the eyes of the person about to be hanged, or an observer in the crowds, or a narrator about whom you know nothing, or a mixture of these? Does this make a difference to who you feel sympathetic towards?

2. Using your notes and underlinings, talk about the differences and similarities between the two poems, looking particularly at:

- the differences in the poets' attitudes towards hanging;
- what each poet has to say about the effects of a public hanging on the people in the crowd;
- the ways in which the poets direct your sympathies;
- what aspects of the scene and events the poets encourage you to focus on;
- what kind of picture of the scene is created and what kind of language each poet uses help you to picture the scene;
- what feelings each poem arouses in you about hanging.

Ideas for Writing

Write about the differences and similarities between the two poems. Try to write at least one paragraph about each of the issues you discussed in the last activity. Use your annotations on the poems themselves to give you evidence to back up the points you make.

Work on the Anthology as a Whole

Using this Section

This section contains a number of alternative ways of exploring any single poem. It also suggests a range of activities for reading and responding to the anthology as a whole.

LONG-SONG SELLER.

(From a Daguerreotype by BEARD.*)*

"Three yards a penny! Three yards a penny! Beautiful songs! Newest songs! Popular songs! Three yards a penny! Songs, songs, songs!"

Exploring a Poem (1)

Your group should have one copy of the poem on a large piece of sugar paper, a copy of the poem for each group member and some felt tips.

Appoint one person to be a scribe for the group.

1. Before you start to read the poem, see if it has a title. If it does, your group should begin by jotting down any words and phrases which you associate with the title. Your scribe should write down your ideas near the title on the sugar paper.

2. Now listen to one person in the group reading the poem out loud. Think of the words you wrote about the title, but don't worry if it does not make much sense at this stage- this first reading is just to get a general idea.

3. Each person should now read the poem silently to themselves. (You may need to do this more than once.)

4. At this stage you still may not be able to make sense of the whole poem but you are probably forming ideas about parts of it.

On your copy of the poem:

- Underline any words or references which you did not understand and put a question mark by the side of them.
- Underline with a straight line any words or phrases which you think are probably important to the meaning of the poem. (You do not have to know why they are important, just trust your own instincts.)
- Underline with a wavy line any words or phrases which you like, or which strike you as interesting or startling.

5. When each person has done this, come back together as a group. Each person should now read out the words they did not understand and the scribe should write them in a column on the sugar paper. Can you help each other with these words?

6. When you have done this, each person should read out the other words and phrases they underlined and the scribe should enter them on the poem, using the same system of straight and wavy lines.

7. Now spend some time looking at what you have got. What connections can you find between the words and phrases which have been underlined? If there are some, indicate this by drawing lines with the felt tips. (Make sure you include the words you wrote near the title at the beginning of this session.)

8. When you feel you have talked enough you might like to hear the poem read again. In any case you now need to bring together your notes and your reading of the poem, and see what conclusions you have reached. You could just talk about this, or you could consider some or all of the questions below:

- How would you describe the mood and atmosphere of this poem?
- What feelings did the poem arouse in you as you read and thought about it?
- How did the poet make you respond in the way you did?
- Whose voice seems to be speaking in the poem?
- What do you think this poem is saying to you?

Exploring a Poem (2)

1. In your group read the poem aloud once or twice.

2. On your own, underline any words or phrases that stood out when you were reading or listening that:

- made a strong impression on you;
- you didn't really understand;
- linked up somehow with other words or phrases.

Now tell each other what you noticed.

3. Can you say anything about the shape of the poem? How are the words laid out on the page?

4. Think about the voice in the poem. What can you say about its tone - is it sad, happy or angry? How many voices are there? What sort of person does it belong to?

5. Can you list any emotions or feelings that are present in the poem?

6. Is the ending of the poem surprising or thought-provoking in any way?

7. For reporting back to the rest of the class try to complete the following:

One of the things this poem seems to be saying to us is..........

but we're still not sure about............

Performing Poems

All poems need to be read aloud, but some poems can be fun to perform as a small group. Performance can bring out all sorts of new ideas and ways of reading the poem. It can bring the poem to life for other people, as well as being enjoyable for the performers. These are some guidance notes to help you to plan a performance.

Performing a poem is a dramatic presentation, using voices but also it can involve any of the other techniques you might expect in a piece of drama (sound effects, music, props, costume, staging etc.) You should prepare for the performance in the way that a director and actors prepare a play for the theatre. Each person in the group needs to think of themselves as an actor/director, not just a reader.

To plan your performance you will each need a copy of the poem and a pen or pencil to mark on your copy any decisions you make about who's reading when and how.

Here is one way of planning and rehearsing your performance:

1. Choose one person to read the poem aloud to everyone else.

2. Choose a second person to read it aloud, to allow you to start to get to know the poem.

3. Spend a little time talking about your first impressions of the poem. You could do this by raising questions about the poem. For instance:

> 'Is it about ......?
> Why do you think that word is used?
> What does that mean?
> Who's speaking?

Talk about the questions raised and pool your ideas.

4. Talk about how you could divide the poem up so that everyone is involved in the performance. Don't just do it in equal chunks to give everyone the same amount. Do it in a way that will help bring out the meanings in the poem.

Just because a poem seems to have only one voice in it doesn't mean that it is best read by one person. Think of ways of emphasising particular words of phrases by using more than one voice. You could even have more than one voice at the same time.

5. Do a first run through and then discuss how it went. Make changes to improve it. Think about extra things that would help to bring the poem to life and make it enjoyable to watch as well as hear. Be brave about adding in actions or props or sound effects.

6. Now rehearse your performance carefully, making changes as you go. As you get to know the poem better, don't be afraid to suggest alternative ways of doing it. You might suddenly notice something about the meaning that you hadn't thought of before.

If you have time, you could pause before each change of reader, to give suggestions to each reader about ways of developing that bit of the reading.

After the Performance

If all of the groups in the class did performances of the same poem, talk about the differences between them.

- Did any of the performances make you see new things in the poem or change your view of the poem? Make a list of all the good ideas in other people's performances.

- What did you think of your own performance? Evaluate it in terms of:
  - what it did to suggest the meanings in the poem;
  - how well the voices worked;
  - how pleased you were with the acting/reading;
  - what you thought of your use of staging, sound effects etc.;
  - what you would do differently if you were to do it again?

If the groups did performances of different poems:

- Choose one performance that you particularly enjoyed. Look back at the poem in the anthology and talk about how the performance brought it to life for you. Talk about anything you might have done differently.

- Evaluate your own performance, using the suggestions listed above.

Ideas for Writing

1. Write about the differences between the performances of the same poem. Write about your ideas and feelings about the poem and how the different performances matched up to your ideas. Evaluate your own performance and write about the experience of performing the poem and what you learnt from it.

2. Write up your performance as a shooting script for a short 'Poems at Bedtime' programme for Channel 4, in which a different poem is dramatised every night for a month. In adapting your performance for TV, you could add in all kinds of things that TV would make possible, such as visual images, showing bits of the text on the screen whilst the reading is taking place and so on. You could design the title sequence, choosing an image or images to suggest something about the poem.

Re-organising the Anthology into Themes

This anthology has been organised in chronological order. In other words, it starts with the earliest poem, an Anglo-Saxon riddle and ends with a poem written in the early twentieth century.

It could have been organised differently. Many anthologies group poems by theme. If you were going to re-organise the anthology by theme, what theme headings would you choose?

1. Go through the anthology, looking at the poems and decide on what subjects and themes are dealt with in the poems. Discuss alternative headings for the themes. For instance, there might be a heading about Love/Relationships/Sexuality/ Male and Female Lives/Marriage. Which of these headings would you choose? Would you want more than one of them?

2. Choose one of your theme headings to explore more fully. List all of the poems that you think should be included under your heading.
Read all of the poems under your heading.
Find two that strike you as similar in some way.
Make a chart headed:

Similarities	Differences

Use it to record what you notice in comparing the two poems.

3. Prepare a reading of the poems and an oral presentation in which you:

- describe the similarities and differences between the two poems;
- say why you chose the two poems and what you like about them.

Making Your Own Selection of Poems (1)

Dip into the anthology, reading whatever takes your fancy and noting down titles of poems you particularly like.
Pick your three favourite poems. Share them with a partner.
Try doing any of these things with your poems:

- learn one of them off by heart to recite to the class;
- do a drawing/painting that expresses the ideas/the feelings/the images in one of the poems;
- prepare a reading/performance of your collection of six poems, with a brief introduction to the reading and to each of the poems.

Making Your Own Selection of Poems (2)

Working as pairs, choose two poems to be read at each of the following occasions:

- a Valentine's Day party;
- a funeral;
- a poetry reading for parents, organised by the PTA;
- an event to raise money for a war-torn country.

Join up with another pair. Compare your choices and justify them to each other.

Making Your Own Selection of Poems (3)

Produce your own shorter collection of no more than ten poems, selected from the anthology. Think about the reasons behind your choice. These are some of the choices open to you:

- choosing poems that you like;
- choosing poems that deal with the same theme or choosing poems about different themes;
- choosing poems from a range of different periods or concentrating on just one period;
- choosing humorous poems;
- choosing poems that argue a viewpoint;
- choosing poems which are all by male poets, or all by female poets, or a mixture.

When you have chosen your poems, present them as an anthology, with an Introduction, explaining your choice and saying something about the poems which will get the reader interested.

Do some research to see if you can find out anything about the poets of your ten poems. Decide whether any of this information would be interesting to present to your readers. You could put it alongside each poem, or at the back of the anthology.

Design a cover for the anthology that suggests something about the kinds of poems you have chosen.
Decide whether to include drawings or other visual material to go with each poem. You could use images from magazines or do your own illustrations.
If you have access to a computer, decide on what kind of typeface would be most appropriate for your poems. You could use one single typeface or vary it from poem to poem.

Disgusted of Tonbridge Wells.....

Some of these poems could cause offence to certain people, because of their language or the topic they deal with or because of the view they express.

In London, a project called 'Poems on the Underground' has bought advertising space on London tube trains and used it to display a wide range of poems. It is part of an attempt to make poetry popular and increase its readership.

Pick three poems which, if they were to be displayed in a public place, such as a tube train, might prompt letters of complaint to a newspaper.

Write the three letters, making sure that the personality of the writer and the reason for the offence are as different as possible.

Then write a reply justifying their selection for publication.

Poems about War and Soldiering

Several poems in the anthology, from the sixteenth century right through to the nineteenth century are about the experience of war. Skim through the anthology listing any poems that are about war. Many of the poems are either anti-war, or are about what it is really like to be called up as a soldier and expected to fight.

A Short Role-Play

You have been invited to the first meeting of an organisation called 'Ghosts against War'. The ghosts of people involved in wars through the ages have agreed to come and talk to a modern audience about their experience of war and express their view of it. The modern audience includes some people who have come along to argue against pacificism.

Read the poems and divide up the roles amongst the class, with some people acting as the modern audience and either supporting the ghosts in their testimonies, or arguing with them.

These roles are just suggestions. You can also make up ones of your own.

The Volunteer
Joshua Sylvester, the poet
Anne Finch, the poet
a recruited soldier
a recruited soldier's wife
Celia Whitehead, the poet

Copy Acknowledgements
We are grateful to the following for permission to reproduce peoms:
Gerard Benson for a translation of 'An Anglo-Saxon Riddle'.
Faber and Faber for Richard Hamer's translation of 'An Anglo-Saxon Riddle'.
Harper Collins for 'Come live with me and be my love'.